CAMERON
DRISCOLL

KATHLEE
DRISCECC

CAMERON
DRISCEOLL
FATHLEE
PRESCOFU

DISNEY PRINCESS

ARIEL

COMICS COLLECTION

JOE BOOKS LTD

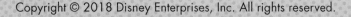

Published simultaneously in the United States and Canada by Joe Books Ltd,
489 College Street, Suite 203, Toronto, ON M6G 1A5.

www.joebooks.com

First Joe Books edition: July 2018

Print ISBN: 978-1-77275-908-2

Library and Archives Canada Cataloguing in Publication
information is available upon request.

Printed and bound in Canada
1 3 5 7 9 10 8 6 4 2

TABLE OF CONTENTS

Ariel

Collects human objects

Curious about the ocean
and the human world

Explores with her friend Flounder

Loves music

Prince Eric

Loves Ariel very much

Prince of a seaside kingdom

Helps her learn about life on land

Flounder

Ariel's closest and most loyal friend

Joins Ariel on her
undersea adventures

Fascinated by human
objects, just like Ariel

Sebastian

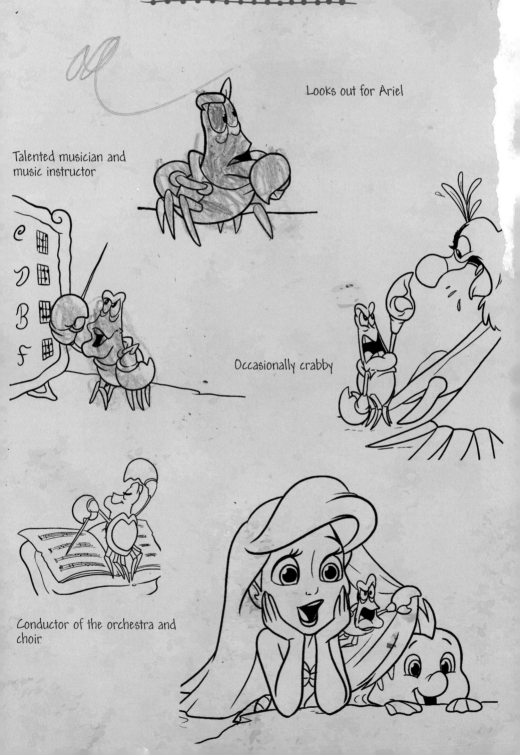

Looks out for Ariel

Talented musician and music instructor

Occasionally crabby

Conductor of the orchestra and choir

UNDER THE SEA

Shark Dreams

OOH! A CAVE!

YOU NEVER CAN GUESS WHAT YOU'LL FIND, ONLY THAT IT'S GOING TO BE SOMETHING SPECIAL!

MAYBE SOMETHING NEW, OR SOMETHING OLD AND LOST...

...OR MAYBE A DEAD END.

I THINK I HEAR SOMETHING!

I JUST HAVE TO KNOW WHAT'S ON THE OTHER SIDE!

YIPES!

CAP'N! THE HOLE IS FLOODING!

THE ISLAND IS SINKING!

IT'S CLEAR THE MERMAID IS TAUNTING US, MEN. OAK ISLAND IS *CURSED!*

BEST WE LEAVE NOW. WE CAN RETURN FOR OUR TREASURE ANOTHER DAY.

IT SOUNDS LIKE THEY'RE JUST LEAVING ALL THIS BEHIND.

MAYBE THEIR TREASURE IS *CURSED!*

THAT'S SILLY. THESE ARE JUST *THINGS*, AND NOW THEY CAN'T GET TO THEM. THIS IS MY FAULT.

I KNOW HOW I CAN HELP! BUT IT'LL REQUIRE A LOT OF DIGGING!

LUCKILY, WE KNOW WHERE EVERYTHING IS BURIED.

THREE SEPARATE BATCHES OF TREASURE, SO EVEN IF SOMEONE FINDS ONE, THEY'LL NEVER FIND IT *ALL!*

THANK GOODNESS FOR THESE TUNNELS! THERE! ALL IN ONE BIG, NEW PLACE!

Sunken Treasure

A-HA! I *KNEW* THERE WAS ONE I HADN'T EXPLORED YET! COME ON.

ARIEL, YA EVER WONDER WHY THESE THINGS KEEP ENDING UP DOWN HERE?

I'VE BEEN THINKING THE ANSWER LIES IN THE WHOOZITS, BUT I NEED MORE SPECIMENS.

IF THIS IS TREASURE, HUMANS SURE DO LOSE A LOT OF IT!

FINDERS KEEPERS, FLOUNDER. LITTLE HELP?

FLOUNDER! COME HERE! I'VE FOUND A MAP!

LOOK, THERE ARE MONSTERS AND SERPENTS AND A BIG STAR ON IT.

THOSE DON'T LOOK LIKE ANYTHING DOWN HERE.

I KNOW. THEY MUST BE LAND CREATURES!

FROM THIS MYSTERIOUS ISLAND CALLED "X"! WE GOTTA FIND IT!

WHATEVER IS IN HERE MUST BE *REALLY* IMPORTANT!

UGH!

WOOOOW, WE HIT THE JACKPOT, FLOUNDER! IS THAT WHAT I THINK IT IS...?

I GOT A *JAR OF DIRT!!*

WHOA, DON'T DROP IT!

IT'S MUSIC TO ME

Homework

ARIEL, I SEE YOU ARE KEEPING UP ON YOUR HOMEWORK?

I AM! LOOK! I'M MAKING A MAP!

AND YOU EXPLORED THE AREAS I ASSIGNED?

OF COURSE! WHY?

BECAUSE "HERE THERE BE" NO MONSTERS *I'VE* EVER SEEN.

I THOUGHT SOME MONSTERS WOULD MAKE THE MAP INTRIGUING!

THE POINT OF THESE ASSIGNMENTS IS TO EDUCATE YOU, FILL YOUR HEAD WITH WHAT YOU'LL NEED TO GET BY IN LIFE.

BUT WHAT IF WHAT I NEED IN LIFE IS ADVENTURE?

YOU DON'T SEE MY PROBLEM AS A PROBLEM, DO YOU?

THERE WAS SO LITTLE OUT THERE TO LOOK AT. I HAD TO DRAW *SOMETHING!*

THERE WAS NOTHING BUT ROCKS AND CORAL AND MORE ROCKS.

THOSE BORING *DETAILS* ARE *MARKERS* SO PEOPLE DON'T GET LOST.

HOW CAN ANYONE DISCOVER SOMETHING NEW IF THEY DON'T GET LOST LOOKING?

BY BORROWING SOMEONE ELSE'S MAP.

DID YOU SEE ANY INTERESTING ANIMALS WHILE YOU WERE OUT?

A STAR DRAGON! IT LOOKED LIKE A COLOSSAL SEA HORSE WITH STARFISH SKIN!

AND IT WAS HUGE! WHEN IT SWUNG ITS TAIL, THE *TIDES CHANGED!*

DID YOU REALLY SEE THAT?

NO, JUST A WHALE LOOKING FOR EXOTIC PLANKTON.

I WAS HOPING YOU WOULD FIND SOMETHING THAT INSPIRED YOU TO LEARN. YOU'RE SMART, BUT RARELY APPLY YOURSELF TO YOUR EDUCATION.

AT LEAST TOMORROW I KNOW YOU'LL GIVE YOUR ALL FOR SEBASTIAN'S MUSIC CLASS.

OH! WE'RE LEARNING A NEW SONG ABOUT AN OCTOPUS! HIS EIGHT ARMS LINE UP WITH THE EIGHT NOTES IN THE SCALE!

I HAVE TO READ UP ON THEM SO I CAN DO THE PIECE JUSTICE.

SO YOU--

SHH! PLEASE! LEARNING!

Music Class

WOW, THIS ONE HAS A LOT OF CORDS!

CHORDS ARE WHEN YOU HOLD SOME DOWN TO ADJUST THE SOUND, THEN PLAY THEM ALL AT ONCE!

I *TOLD* YOU, CHILD, THESE ARE CALLED *STRINGS.* NOW PAY ATTENTION!

ALL AT ONCE? THIS IS IMPOSSIBLE!

PERHAPS WE TRY THE FLUTE.

AHHH AH SUB MARI...

...ET CHORO LUDENTIUM!

Something to Sing About

ARIEL, A SONG MUSTN'T COME FROM THE LISTENER. IT HAS TO COME FROM *YOU.*

TO SPEAK TO THE SOUL, IT HAS TO *COME* FROM THE SOUL!

NOW TELL ME, GIRL...WHAT INSPIRES YOUR PASSION FOR LIFE?

I FOUND ONE OF *THESE!* ISN'T IT *NEAT?*

MARVELOUS.

LET'S TAKE A LOOK AT YOUR LYRICS.

"OOOOH YA-YAH, NO-NO, HEY-HEY. LA-LA-LA, YEAH-YEAH, WOO."

THE WOO IS UNDERLINED. LIKE *WOO!*

YES, I SEE DAT.

I WAS WORKING ON THE REFRAIN.

YES, WELL, YOU SHOULD REFRAIN FROM WRITING LYRICS LIKE DESE.

Can't Tuna Fish

What Are Friends For

FLOUNDER, LOOK! A NEW SHIPWRECK WE HAVEN'T EX--

~WULP~

SEBASTIAAAAANN...

ALL DAT ACADEMY TRAINING...

WHOZITS AND WHATZITS

Human Maps

What the Wick

SCUTTLE, YOU'LL NEVER BELIEVE WHAT WE FOUND TODAY!

THAT MAKES TWO OF US, SWEETIE.

DO YOU KNOW WHAT THIS IS?

OH, WHAT? *THIS?* OF COURSE I KNOW WHAT THIS IS!

AFTER ALL, I AM A *CERTIFICATIONAL* AUTHORITY ON HUMAN STUFF.

IT'S REMARKABLE HOW THEY MANAGE TO GET *ANOTHER BIRD* INTO HERE.

YOU KNOW WHAT I THINK IT IS? AN OBSTACLE COURSE FOR FISH!

WHAT ON EARTH ARE YOU TALKING ABOUT, MON?

WATCH ME JUMP IT!

UH, HOW ABOUT A LITTLE HELP HERE?

DIS WHOLE DAY JUST KEEPS GETTING STRANGER.

SCUTTLE, YOU'LL NEVER BELIEVE WHAT WE FOUND TODAY!

THAT MAKES TWO OF US, SWEETIE.

DO YOU KNOW WHAT THIS IS?

OH, WHAT? *THIS?* OF COURSE I KNOW WHAT THIS IS!

AFTER ALL, I AM A *CERTIFICATIONAL* AUTHORITY ON HUMAN STUFF.

IT'S REMARKABLE HOW THEY MANAGE TO GET *ANOTHER BIRD* INTO HERE.

CALLED... A *FLIBBERBOBBIN*.

LET'S SAY A HUMAN GETS THEIR CLOTHES WET.

THEY HATE THAT.

THEY JUST HANG THEIR WET WEARABLES OFF THIS OL' FLIBBERBOBBIN. IN A FEW HOURS, THEIR CLOTHES GO FROM SOAKING WET TO A LITTLE MOIST. JUST THE WAY HUMANS LIKE!

SO COOL...

DAT IS DE CRAZIEST MUMBO JUMBO I HAVE EVER HEARD.

WOW...

SEBASTIAN, WHAT ARE YOU DOING HERE?

YOU ARE LATE TO REHEARSAL FOR DE SPRING CONCERT. *AGAIN.* THE PIKE WHO PLAYS FIFE SPOTTED YOU WERE HERE.

AND IF YOU PAID ATTENTION IN MUSIC CLASS, YOU WOULD KNOW DIS HAS GOT TO BE A MUSICAL INSTRUMENT. LISTEN,

YOU'RE CRAZY! HOW ARE YOU SUPPOSED TO MAKE MUSIC WITH A *CLOTHES DRYER?*

CLEARLY, IT IS BROKEN.

OH, ARIEL LEFT THIS HERE. I'VE GOTTA GET IT BACK TO HER!

!

KER-POW!!

TOO BAD. A PERFECTLY GOOD FLIBBERBOBBIN RUINED BY THE ELEMENTS.

SPLOOSH!

Treasure Hunt

ARIEL! I JUST HEARD DADDY MENTION THAT THERE ARE PIRATES IN THE CARIBBEAN SEA!

OOH, THEY DROP ALL KINDS OF SHINY THINGS!

OH REALLY? WELL... GOOD FOR THEM! I'M SURE THE CARIBBEAN SEA IS NO PLACE FOR A MERMAID PRINCESS.

AM I RIGHT?

IF WE CATCH THE TIDE NOW, WE'LL BE BACK BY DINNER.

LEMME GET MY BAG!!

Technicality

ThinKap

What the People Know

Going Downhill

Making a Splash

Fin-tastic

YOU CARE [TO] DANCE?

I HAVEN'T HAD LEGS FOR VERY LONG-- I STILL FEEL LIKE I HAVE TWO LEFT FINS.

FINS?

SEE? I CAN'T EVEN TALK LIKE A SURFACE PERSON.

MAYBE YOU CAN SING INSTEAD?

NOW THAT I CAN DO! EVEN WITH ONE FIN TIED BEHIND MY BACK.

Morning Swim

Amazing Feats

LOOK HOW HIGH THE SAND DUNES ARE!

COME ON, ERIC! I'LL RACE YOU TO THE TOP!

HA-HA, WAIT FOR ME!

YOU'RE UP THERE *ALREADY?* WHAT AN AMAZING FEAT!

THEY ARE, AREN'T THEY?

Turn the page
for more giggles from
your favorite
princesses!

Endings

A Dish Served Cold

DISNEY PRINCESS

COMIC STRIPS COLLECTIONS

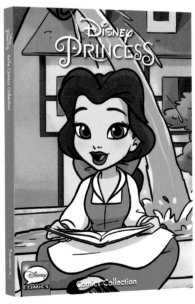

COLLECT THEM ALL!

Written by Paul Benjamin, Steffie Davis, Geoffrey Golden,
Megan Kearney, Amy Mebberson, and Patrick Storck.

Illustrated by Egle Bartolini, Dylan Bonner, Chris Dreier,
Brianna Garcia, Nolen Lee, and Amy Mebberson.

Colored by Wes Dzioba, Paul Little, and Amy Mebberson.

Series edited by Steffie Davis, Jen Hale, Deanna McFadden, and Allison O'Toole.

Lettered by AndWorld Design and Andrew A. Thomas.

Special thanks to Eugene Paraszczuk, Julie Dorris, Chris Troise, Manny Mederos,
Jean-Paul Orpinas, Deron Bennett, Jesse Post, and Amy Weingartner.

You can collect a world of comic adventure!

EACH SET SOLD SEPARATELY.

Disney PRINCESS
BELLE

Disney PRINCESS
RAPUNZEL

Disney PRINCESS
POCAHONTAS

ARIEL & FRIENDS

MAGIC CARPET RIDE

What if you could let your favorite
Disney Princess know how her
story helped inspire you?

Learn more at DearPrincess.Disney.com